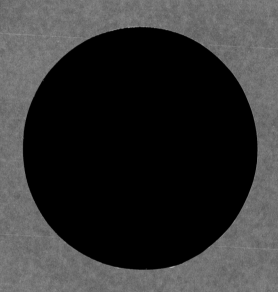

I spy with my little eye…

EDWARD GIBBS

Brubaker, Ford & Friends

AN IMPRINT OF THE TEMPLAR COMPANY LIMITED

I spy with my little eye…

something
that is **blue**.

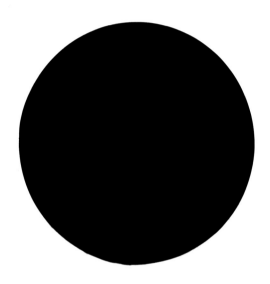

I am the
biggest animal in
the whole world.

I spy with my little eye...

something
that is **grey**.

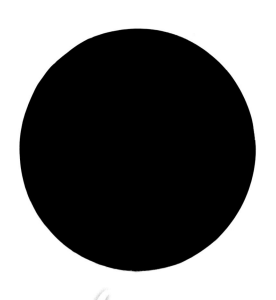

I have a very
long trunk.

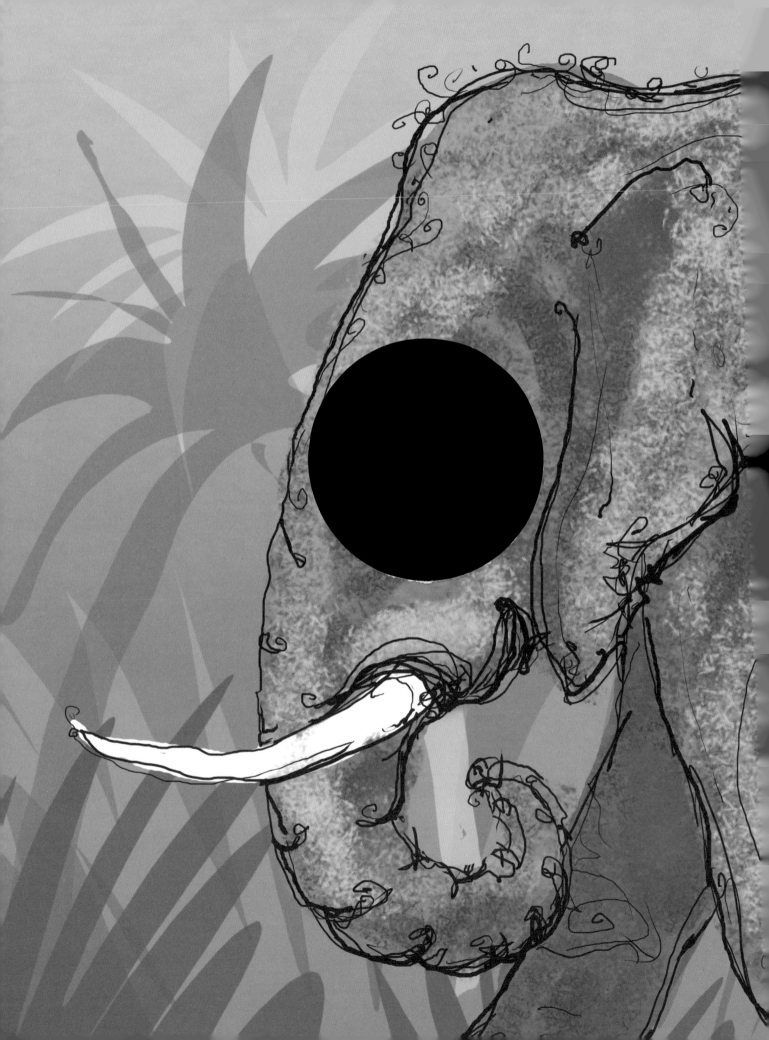

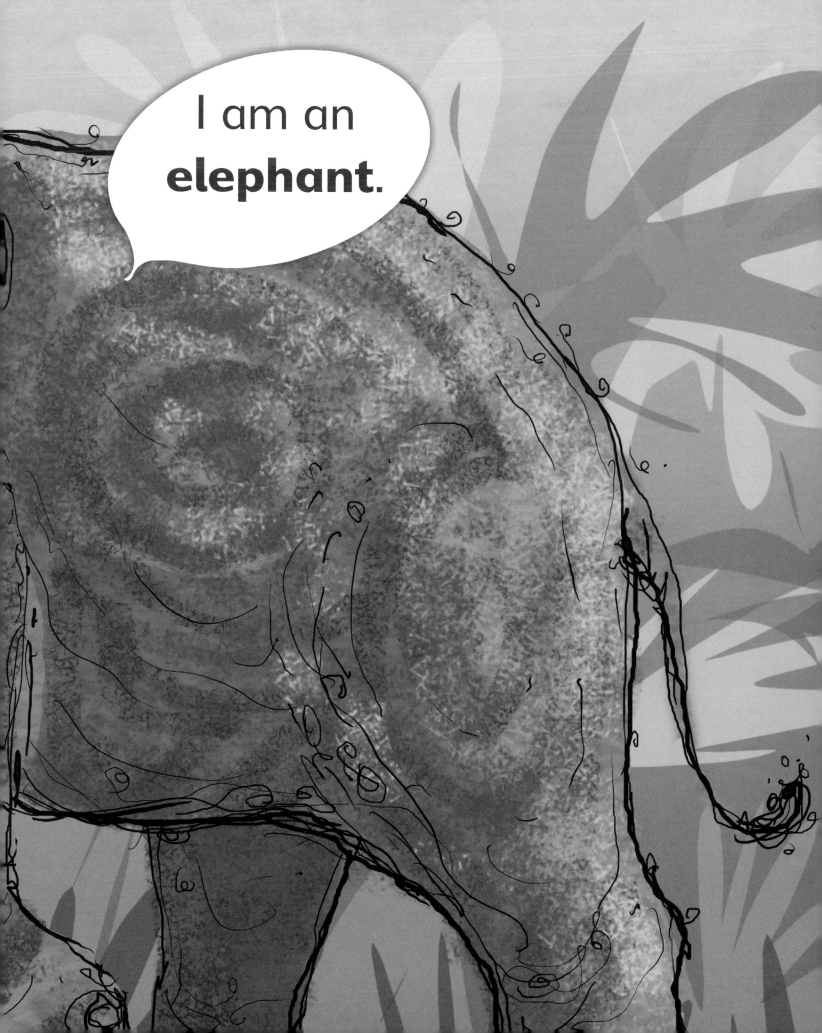

I spy with my little eye...

something
that is **white**.

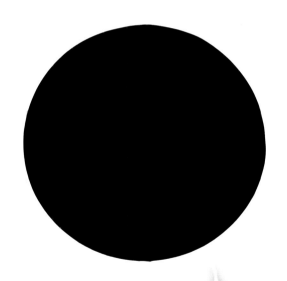

The North Pole
is my home.

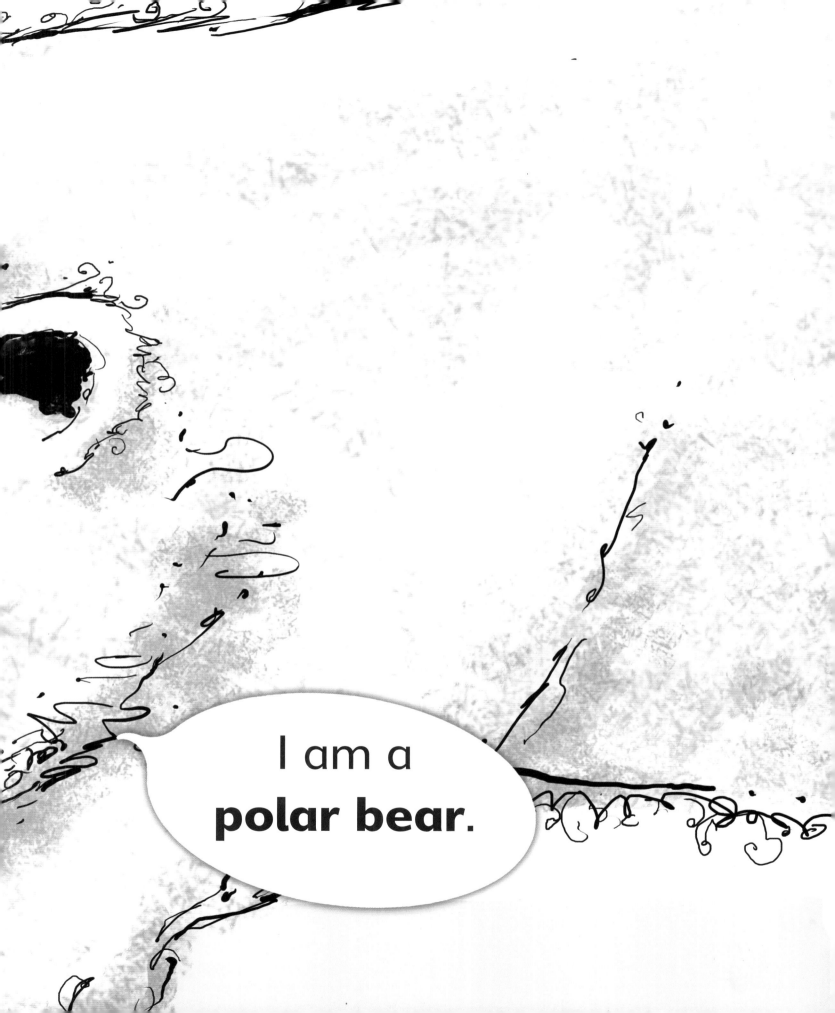

I spy with my little eye…

something
that is **yellow**.

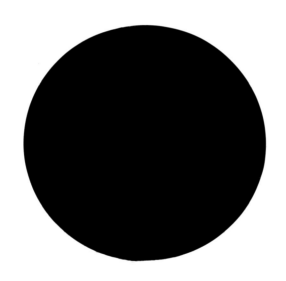

I am the king
of the jungle —
hear me ROAR!

I spy with my little eye...

something
that is **orange**.

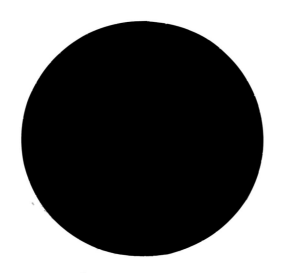

I swing
from tree to
tree with my

I spy with my little eye...

something
that is **red**.

I have

a long

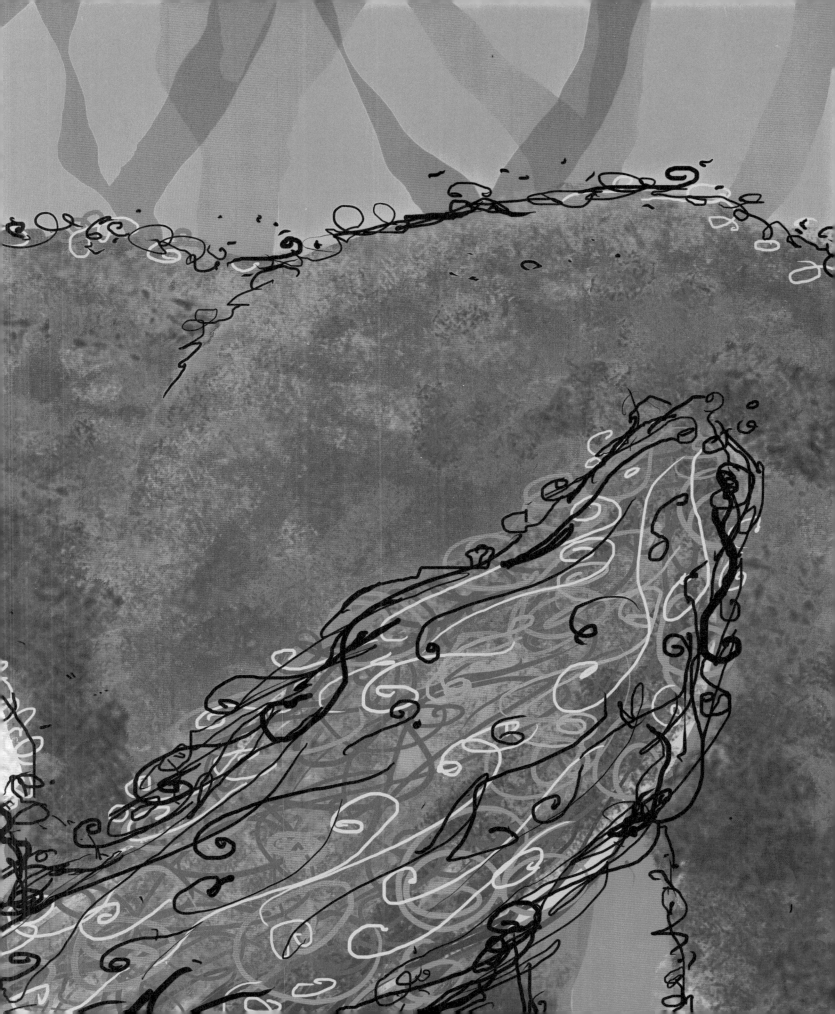

I spy with my little eye...

something
that is **green**.

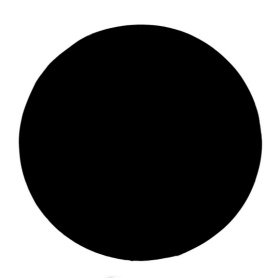

I hop about on
my long legs.

What can **you** spy with **your** little eye?

To Léonard and Mélinda

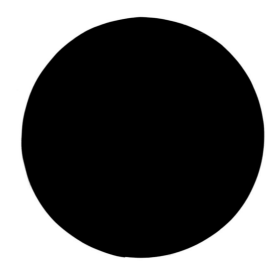

A BRUBAKER, FORD & FRIENDS BOOK,
an imprint of The Templar Company Limited

First published in the UK in 2011 by Templar Publishing,
The Granary, North Street, Dorking, Surrey, RH4 1DN, UK
www.templarco.co.uk

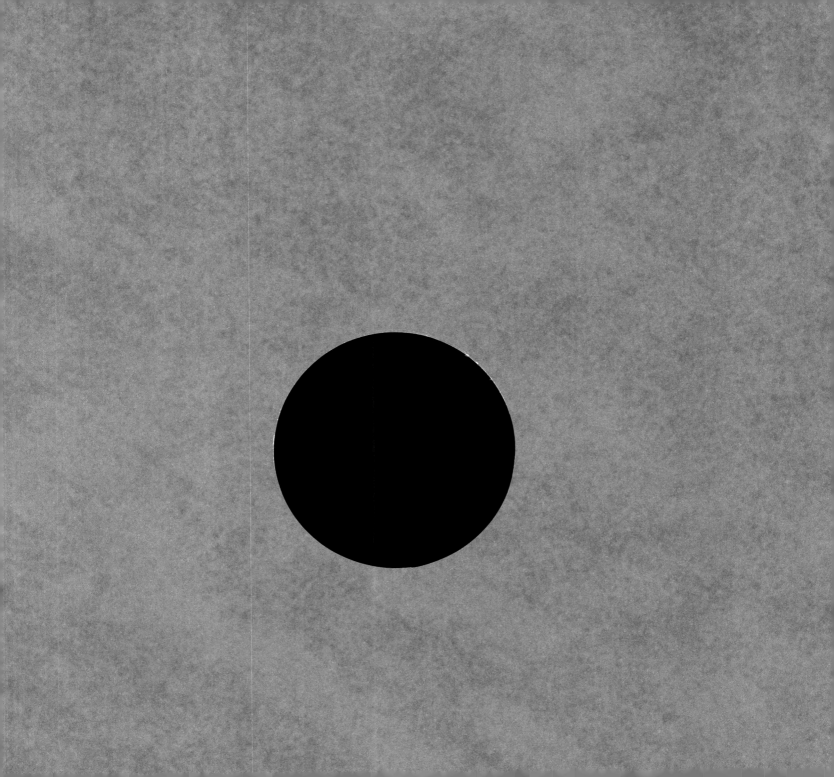

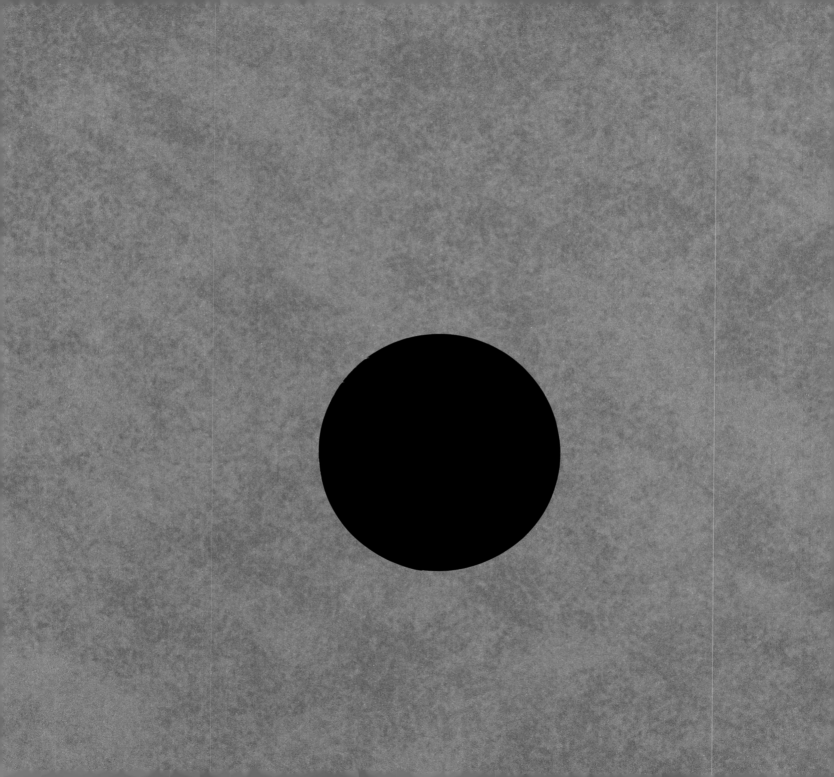